ORSON'S FARM™
PULLS THE PLOUGH

D1638213

ℛℛ
RAVETTE BOOKS

This edition first published by Ravette Books Limited 1989

Printed and bound in Great Britain
for Ravette Books Limited,
3 Glenside Estate, Star Road, Partridge Green,
Horsham, West Sussex RH13 8RA
by Cox & Wyman Ltd, Reading

ISBN 1 85304 175 0

© 1988 United Feature Syndicate, Inc

OH, RHETT! OH, RHETT! YOU CAN'T LEAVE ME NA-OW!!

RUMMAGE
RUMMAGE
RUMMAGE

THUD

© 1988 United Feature Syndicate, Inc.

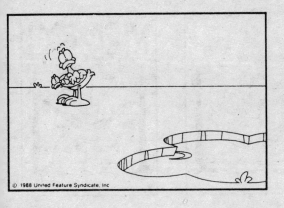

© 1988 United Feature Syndicate, Inc.

VICTORY!

JIM DAVIS   10-17

FWOONG

SPLAT

JIM DAVIS   10-18

© 1988 United Feature Syndicate, Inc.

C
L
O
P

JIM DAVIS   10-19

© 1988 United Feature Syndicate, Inc.

JPM DAVIS
10-20

JIM DAVIS   10-21

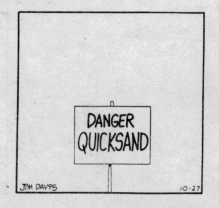

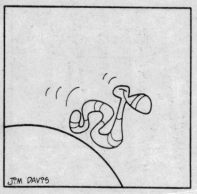

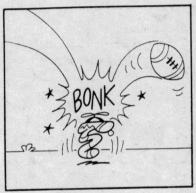

JIM DAVIS   11-15

© 1988 United Feature Syndicate, Inc.

OINK! OINK! OINK!
REEK! GRUNT! SNORT

JIM DAVIS   11-17

EVERY ONCE IN A WHILE, A PIG'S JUST GOTTA DO THAT

© 1988 United Feature Syndicate inc

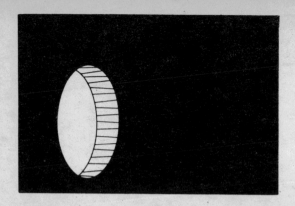

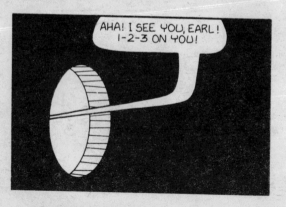

GRAB

© 1986 United Feature Syndicate, Inc

HEY, GUYS, LET'S HAVE AN UGLY FACE CONTEST

YOU MIGHT AS WELL GIVE ME THE TROPHY NOW, PIG. WATCH THIS

OH YEAH?!

ROY'S LAWN ORNAMENTS

$4.99

BRETT KOTH

KLONK

© 1988 United Feature Syndicate, Inc.

12-15

BRETT KOTH

JIM DAVIS

© 1988 United Feature Syndicate, Inc

BRETT KOTH   JIM DAVIS 12-21

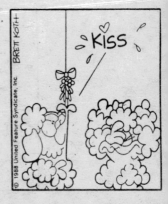

© 1988 United Feature Syndicate, Inc.

© 1988 United Feature Syndicate, Inc.

BRETT KOTH

JIM DAVIS 12·24

THOCK

DONK WHAP BAM
DONK WHAP BAM
DONK BAM
DONK

JIM DAVIS

FLUNDGE

AVALANCHE ZONE

© 1988 United Feature Syndicate, Inc.

BRETT KOTH

12-29

12-30

JIM DAVIS

DONK!

© 1988 United Feature Syndicate, Inc.

I LOVE TEASING
THOSE FISH

BRETT KOTH

CHONK

© 1988 United Feature Syndicate, Inc.

1-6-89

JIM DAVIS

© 1988 United Feature Syndicate, Inc.

MOM!

BRETT KOTH

Other Jim Davis books published by Ravette

In this series

Goes Half Hog! 1	£1.95
Goes Half Hog! 2	£1.95
Counts Its Chickens 1	£1.95
Counts Its Chickens 2	£1.95
Rules The Roost 1	£1.95
Rules The Roost 2	£1.95
Sows The Seed	£1.95
Feeds The Flock	£1.95
Cuts The Corn	£1.95

Garfield Pocket books

No. 1	Garfield The Great Lover	£1.95
No. 2	Garfield Why Do You Hate Mondays?	£1.95
No. 3	Garfield Does Pooky Need You?	£1.95
No. 4	Garfield Admit It, Odie's OK!	£1.95
No. 5	Garfield Two's Company	£1.95
No. 6	Garfield What's Cooking?	£1.95
No. 7	Garfield Who's Talking?	£1.95
No. 8	Garfield Strikes Again	£1.95
No. 9	Garfield Here's Looking At You	£1.95
No. 10	Garfield We Love You Too	£1.95
No. 11	Garfield Here We Go Again	£1.95
No. 12	Garfield Life and Lasagne	£1.95
No. 13	Garfield In The Pink	£1.95
No. 14	Garfield Just Good Friends	£1.95
No. 15	Garfield Plays It Again	£1.95
No. 16	Garfield Flying High	£1.95
No. 17	Garfield On Top Of The World	£1.95
No. 18	Garfield Happy Landings	£1.95

All these books are available at your local bookshop or news-agent, or can be ordered direct from the publisher. Just tick the titles you require and fill in the form below. Prices and availability subject to change without notice.

Ravette Books Limited, 3 Glenside Estate, Star Road, Partridge Green, Horsham, West Sussex RH13 8RA
Please send a cheque or postal order, and allow the following for postage and packing. UK: 45p for one book, 20p for a second book and 15p for each additional book.

Name ....

Address ....

....